A FAM
30-DA

Building Bridges

Improving a Troubled Family Relationship

Carol Setter, Ph.D.

Paul Lewis & Thom Black
Series Editors

ZondervanPublishingHouse
Grand Rapids, Michigan

A Division of HarperCollins*Publishers*

Project Overview: *Building Bridges*

Day 1	Day 2	Day 3
Focus on the Problem	A Realistic Assessment of the Problem	Identify Others Affected by the Problem
Part I: Analyze the Situation		
Day 8	Day 9	Day 10
Identify What You Like About the Person	Find Common Ground	The Unexpected Contact
Part III: Survey the Alternatives		
Day 15	Day 16	Day 17
Time to Talk	Create a Partnership for Change	How to Keep Talking
Part V: Implement Your First Plan		
Day 22	Day 23	Day 24
Many Faces	Types of Negotiations	From the Other Side of the Table
Part VI: Consider the Responses		
Day 29	Day 30	Month 2
Be Gentle with Yourself	Commitment	Conclusion
Part VIII: Achieve Long-Term Change		

— Improving a Troubled Family Relationship

Day 4	Day 5	Day 6	Day 7
Identify Projected Outcomes	Thinking About Your Behaviors	Renew Skills in Listening	Brush Up on Body Language
	Part II: Assess Yourself		
Day 11	**Day 12**	**Day 13**	**Day 14**
The Planned Contact	Work with Alternatives	Practice with a Friend	Use a Referee
	Part IV: Evaluate Alternatives		
Day 18	**Day 19**	**Day 20**	**Day 21**
Set Limits on Disagreements	The Power of Praise	Devise an Action Vocabulary	And If You're Both Right . . .
Part V: Implement Your First Plan			
Day 25	**Day 26**	**Day 27**	**Day 28**
Ancient History	Lighten Up	Artful Use of Questions	Seeing the Bigger Picture
	Part VII: Implement Your Second Plan		

Building Bridges

Requests for information should be addressed to:

ZondervanPublishingHouse
Grand Rapids, Michigan 49530

ISBN: 0-310-21588-9

Interior illustrations by Chris Sharp
Interior design by Paul Lewis

Printed in the United States of America

97 98 99 00 01 02 03 04 /❖ LP/ 10 9 8 7 6 5 4 3 2 1

Introduction

A home is not a mere transient shelter: its essence lies in the personalities of the people who live in it.

—*H. L. Mencken*

We are turning away from the notion that family is a place to stay only until one "gets a real life." We are eager for the long-term relationships possible in families, the growing together and nurturing of the ones we love.

Even with this goal in mind, sometimes relationships within our families fail to thrive. You must have had one in mind when you chose this topic. It may be a troubled relationship with a parent, spouse, sibling, or other relative. You would like to make the relationship better, but need ideas.

The goal of this 30-day program is to provide you with ways to analyze your situation and devise your own personal plan. The program is presented in eight sections, with activities for you to do each day.

Most of these techniques are geared for working out a relationship with another adult or older teenager. Applying this process with younger children will require more structure in the interactive steps and age-appropriate activities.

Use this guide as a diary to record your thoughts and organize your actions. The daily activities only take a few moments to do, but they provide you with an opportunity to plan your actions and reflect upon them before implementation. And, since this program is like a diary, you can revisit it and use some of the suggestions from your brainstorming to enrich your relationship beyond the thirty days of this program.

You have an opportunity to consider new ways of talking and relating to your family member to bring about long-term improvement. You've already made a beginning. Keep going!

Part I:
Analyze the Situation
Focus on the Problem

The beginning is the most important part of the work.
—Plato, The Republic, Book II, 377B

DAY 1

To Think About: A relationship with another person can be stable over a number of years and then deteriorate. A series of events may lead to a "sudden" break. One person may have done something to annoy or betray the trust of the other. You may have done or said something you regretted. Or perhaps you and your relative have drifted apart due to physical distance from each other or decreased involvement in once common interests.

To Do: One of the first tasks in repairing a relationship is to look closely at the problem. Over the next few days, we will look at the problem several ways, but for today, you have three tasks.

1. Identify the person with whom you wish to improve a relationship.

   I want to improve my relationship with ______________________.

2. Describe the problem and the attempts you have made to resolve it.

Description of problem	Your efforts to resolve the problem	Results

3. Tell why resolving this problem is so important to you now.

Part I:
Analyze the Situation

A Realistic Assessment of the Problem

The difficulty in life is the choice.
—George Moore, The Bending of the Bough (1900), act IV

DAY 2

To Think About: If you have a relationship that has been broken for some time, you probably have tried to find ways to make it better. One thing to consider, before you go further into this program, is whether this relationship is worth fighting for or whether it is better to let it go. If you are trying to improve a relationship with a person who abuses alcohol or drugs, who has neglected you for years, or who has threatened physical harm, you may be better off to select a relationship that has more promise of success. To evaluate a difficult or complex relationship, you may wish to consult a healthcare professional.

To Do: Take a moment now to describe how long this relationship has been a problem. Be frank with yourself about whether this relationship has realistic potential for improvement. Look back at Day 1. What time period are you describing there? Has there been any improvement over time?

You will have an opportunity today to visualize the journey you are about to make. You are at the starting point and want to get to the end. What barriers are in your pathway? For example, have demands been made—like apologies or actions—that one of you sees as a prerequisite for "forgiveness"? Are apologies required? What are the barriers to improving your relationship? Draw barrier lines on the pathway below and describe them.

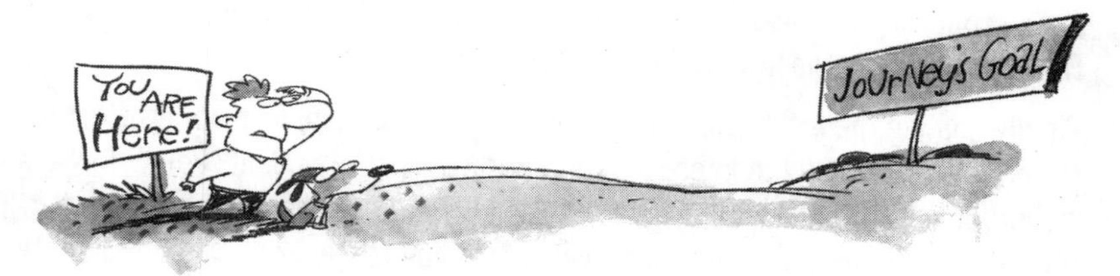

Now go back and look at the barriers you have identified. Are they valid? Could you consider crossing out some of them? Adjust your barriers diagram.

Part I:
Analyze the Situation

Identify Others Affected by the Problem

The voyage of discovery is not in seeking new landscapes but in having new eyes.

—Marcel Proust

To Think About: When two people have a significant break in their relationship, it can affect other family members. People may take sides. The friction may interfere with holiday celebrations and become the focus of family disagreements.

To Do: For your activity today, write your name in one square and your family member's name in another square. Then construct circles around the perimeter and identify other family members or friends who have been affected. Now link these individuals to the primary squares. Use a solid line for a strong relationship and a dotted line for a weak relationship. Refer to the example below, then construct your own model.

Finish your diagram by writing a few words of description on each of the lines. How has the situation affected those around you?

Finally, analyze the total diagram you have created. Are children being affected? Have you been careful to keep them out of the adult "confidant" role? How are you helping them deal with their sense of loss at hearing you speak in unflattering terms about someone they have known and respected? Has the dispute broken the family into "insider-outsider" lines? Are in-laws and cousins being drawn in and enlarging the dispute?

Write down some responsible actions you can take to contain the disagreement or problem.

Part I:
Analyze the Situation

Identify Projected Outcomes

The best thing about the future is that it comes one day at a time.

—Abraham Lincoln

DAY 4

To Think About: Often when we are in a troubled relationship, we have a vague sense that we want things to "get better." However, we never stop to identify how much improvement is satisfactory. For example, if a family member has broken all communications with you, is a weekly phone conversation such a significant improvement that it would satisfy you as a dramatic positive change? Similarly, if your teenage son has refused to tell you where he is going, who he is seeing, and when he will come home—does it satisfy your goal to know more about his schedule and be certain of the truthfulness of the information?

To Do: Today's objective is to identify both short-term and long-term goals for your broken relationship.

In thirty days, I want my relationship with _______________ to change so that:

____

____

____

____

____

____

____

In six months, I want our relationship to be described in the following way:

____

____

____

____

____

____

Take a moment and reread your goals. Are they vague or specific? How will you know when you have achieved your goals? Have you identified changes in behaviors or attitudes? Modify or clarify your goals so that you will definitely know when you have reached them. Can you expand some of your short-term goals into long-term goals? For example, your short-term goal may be to have one phone conversation in the next thirty days, while your six-month goal might be to communicate by phone once per week.

You will focus on your desired outcomes as you organize your individual plan for working with your relative. But see your goals as "works in progress," since you may expand or narrow them as you work through the process.

Part II:
Assess Yourself

Think About Your Behaviors

If we don't change our direction, we're likely to end up where we're headed.

—Chinese Proverb

DAY 5

To Think About: Today is the first of three days to assess your responses to the conflict. For example, some individuals play the part of the victim. They feel wronged and expect others to make amends. They insist on an apology and changes the other individual must make in order to right the situation. The waiting starts, and the rift widens. Some individuals retreat from conflict and break off both communication and physical contact. For example, two sisters who are arguing may no longer visit each other's families, or they may try to stop their husbands from golfing together. An adult son arguing with his mother may alter vacation plans so that she does not have an opportunity to see her grandchild. Each of these behaviors may be part of an escalation or a "gotcha" type of retribution.

To Do: In the circle below, identify a word or words that describe your feelings, e.g., lonely, angry, vindictive, guilty, fearful, rejected, confused. Choose or come up with your own.

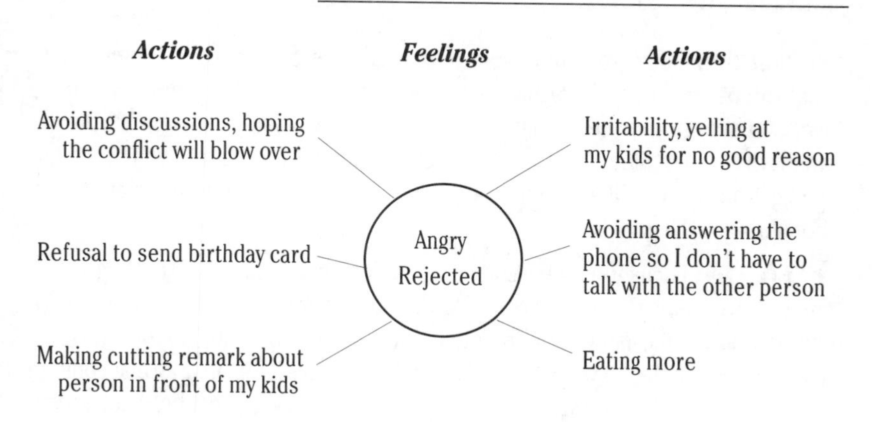

Then out from the circle, identify actions you have taken based upon these feelings.

One situation can lead to many ramifications and changes in behavior. Look at your diagram. See any trends? Did you initiate some hurtful actions? Did you respond to any hurtful actions? Does it matter who initiated hurtful actions?

You are not a "victim"—you are in charge of how you think and respond. So analyze your list. Are you acting in a way that is counterproductive to improving relationships? Can you change some of those actions now to start the healing process? Circle them and write yourself a note about how you plan to change your response.

Part II: Assess Yourself

Renew Skills in Listening

A good listener is not only popular everywhere, but after a while he gets to know something.

—Wilson Mizner

To Think About: When you were a child, your mom and dad may have used golden oldie words to admonish you: "You can't hear with your mouth open." This admonishment may also apply in our disagreements with others. We are so eager to explain our position, to tell our story, to be convincing, that we can't hear and understand what the other person is saying to us. Ever walk out of a disagreement and go over and over in your head all you said and what you wish you had said? Do you spend the same amount of time thinking about what was said to you? True listening is an active skill—one that requires energy, concentration, practice, and thoughtful analysis.

➧ **TO DO:** Focus today on a common problem in listening: interrupting someone else to speak, thereby discounting the other person's words. While you are engaged in your day, monitor two of your conversations. How often do you interrupt? In a spirited debate, do you interrupt more frequently? Keep an informal count in your head of your interruptions. You will probably be on your best behavior, so you may want to also count the times you think about interrupting but stop yourself.

\# of times______ # of times______

Your observations: ____

____

____

What skills can you practice today? Study the following suggestions and rank them from 1–5. Which ones do you most need to include in your active listening skills approach?

Rank	***Skills***
______	After a conversation, repeat to yourself the other person's significant points.
______	Listen with your eyes. Give your full concentration.
______	After listening, pause and consider your response before speaking.

______ Model to others that you are a listener. Remember an informal conversation you had with someone and ask that person how things are going. Refrain from giving advice unless asked.

______ Establish a "listening time" at dinner or bedtime when there are fewer distractions.

Part II: Assess Yourself

Brush Up on Body Language

One that would have the fruit must climb the tree.

—Thomas Fuller

❦ **To Think About:** You are in your boss's office for a planned private discussion. Visualize yourself sitting there. Are you sitting up straight? Alert? Nodding pleasantly? Probably so. In special situations, our bodies can exhibit the appropriate behavior. But at other times it's like someone switched the "automatic" button to "off." When involved in a disagreement, our best intentions for body language fall apart, and we convey negative messages that are louder than our words.

If you anticipate a stressful confrontation with someone, you may want to select certain body language signals to work on in advance. With increased awareness and practice, you may be less likely to slip into negative behaviors.

➧ **To Do:** Body language is the general term for a collection of behaviors that show attitude. For our first activity today, envision your body in a FRAME. Take a moment and study the acrostic below.

FRAME

______ **F**idgeting

______ **R**ejecting (e.g., frown, tightened mouth, arms crossed)

______ **A**voiding eye contact

______ **M**imicking

______ **E**scaping (e.g., pulling back, leaving)

Now, just as you visualized yourself in your employer's office, picture yourself in the two situations you used yesterday for your listening exercise. For each of the FRAME elements,try to remember your body language and give yourself a "–" (you did not exhibit the characteristic) or "+" (you did exhibit the characteristic).

Situation #1

FRAME

_______ **F**idgeting
_______ **R**ejecting (e.g., frown, tightened mouth, arms crossed)
_______ **A**voiding eye contact
_______ **M**imicking
_______ **E**scaping (e.g., pulling back, leaving)

Situation #2

FRAME

_______ **F**idgeting
_______ **R**ejecting (e.g., frown, tightened mouth, arms crossed)
_______ **A**voiding eye contact
_______ **M**imicking
_______ **E**scaping (e.g., pulling back, leaving)

Which characteristics would you like to improve upon?

____

____

For your last activity of today, observe friends, spouse, or co-workers in various situations. What techniques and habits do you observe them using effectively to convey positive body language?

____

____

Part III: Survey the Alternatives

Identify What You Like About the Person

A prudent question is one half of wisdom.

—Francis Bacon

DAY 8

❦ **To Think About:** Once a relationship has soured, we often find ourselves quickly ticking off a list of negative things about the other person. Previous slights, conversations, and actions take on new hostile meanings. For example, suppose you are getting married a year after your sister was married. You perceive her wedding as more lavish than yours due to her financial manipulation of your parents. Old feelings of competitiveness and favoritism are stirred afresh. Harsh words between you have caused a rift.

In order to move beyond these negative feelings (whether warranted or not), the heat of the situation needs to decrease. One way to do this is to step back and view the larger picture. Ask yourself one very prudent question: "What are the things that once attracted me to this person?"

To Do: Flip through the memories in your mind. Find a picture of you and the other person in happier times. Sketch that picture in the photo frame below. What are you doing? What are you talking about? Are you alone together? Who's around? Why are you happy?

Now, around the border of the picture, write as quickly as you can the positive things you can remember about the person and the experience.

Can you think of a favorite joke you shared? A funny secret? Jot it here.

Part III: Survey the Alternatives

Find Common Ground

What breaks in a moment may take years to mend.

—Swedish proverb

DAY 9

To Think About: In the last activity, you looked to the past to find the positive personality traits about your family member. In this lesson, you look to the future. As you work to reestablish your friendship and positive communication, what will the two of you be sharing? What will you be doing? For example, if you used to go camping in the past, will you do that together in the future? Are either of you even interested in camping now? Would trying to recapture old times be a forced activity? Should you be building for the future instead?

To Do: In the think bubble below, take a moment to recall the activities the two of you most enjoyed doing together. Jot down as many as you can, as quickly as you can.

Now, think of the seasons of next year. What might the two of you do together? Go to ball games, ski in the winter, have a Fourth of July picnic? Brainstorm activities based upon what you shared in the past and upon your changing interests. Put some creative thought into your future with this person. Consider a wide variety of formal and informal things you might do together. For example, you might go mall walking, attend a woodworking class, go hiking, plan a day to look for antiques, donate time together at a homeless shelter, exchange quilt pieces for the new babies in your family. Come up with at least two activities for every season. Be creative!

Part III: Survey the Alternatives

The Unexpected Contact

The first step is always to succeed in becoming surprised —to notice that there is something funny going on.

—*David Gelernter,* The Muse in the Machine

DAY 10

To Think About: In the past two days, we have reviewed what we liked about a particular family member and activities we would enjoy doing with that person in the future. If, however, your relationship has been broken for a significant period of time, you may be wondering how you can take that first step toward reconciliation. This will be the focus of our activities today and tomorrow.

Most of us enjoy being surprised: flowers on our birthday, a neighbor who shares cookies with us, a child who gets up early on a snowy morning and shovels the snow out of the driveway, a funny joke taped to the steering wheel of our car, a fruit basket in an unexpected place. A pleasant surprise can signal our loved one that things are about to change for the better.

To Do: Brainstorm some pleasant surprises you could plan for your family member. If you have trouble thinking of ideas, go back to yesterday's activity. For example, if your shared event is a picnic, you might want to send a note and recipe for next summer's outing. If a common experience is golfing, send an article on improving a swing. If a favorite activity is jazz, send an E-mail message about a cool jazz website where songs can be downloaded. Perhaps you want to plan a surprise taken from this current season's activity list.

Write your ideas here: ____________________

____

____

____

If you are still having trouble, try using some of the following starter sentences. I could surprise my family member by:

- sending this favorite food:

  ____

- faxing this favorite newspaper cartoon:

  ____

- taping this funny picture from our past on the refrigerator:

  ____

- sharing this inspiring story:

  ____

- sending a balloon printed with this message:

  ____

- taping this note onto school lunch money:

  ____

- sending a coupon to rent this movie:

  ____

- attending this school function:

  ____

Most of the above don't require money, but they do require time and planning.

Part III:
Survey the Alternatives

The Planned Contact

Sometimes you gotta create what you want to be a part of.

—Geri Weitzman

DAY 11

To Think About: In addition to the "surprise" contact, you also might want to consider a more structured time to get together and talk. You may need to discuss the issue that is disrupting your relationship and determine what level of interaction and intimacy is possible as you go forward. This meeting could be as informal as a discussion during a walk in the park or as formal as a scheduled time and date to sit down for a discussion.

Depending on the situation, you may find that you want to meet on neutral ground, where neither of you is host nor guest. You may want to avoid a setting where one of you is in an obvious authority position or where disruptions from small children make sustained conversation difficult.

To Do: Consider the four options in the diagram below. Put your initials in the box that describes your preferred setting and level of formality for the conversation. Put your family member's initials in the box you think that person would prefer.

Public Setting Structured Situation	I	II	**Public Setting Informal Discussion**
Private Setting Structured Situation	III	IV	**Private Setting Informal Discussion**

Now, consider your observations. If you were inviting your family member for a meeting about the situation, what setting would put both of you at ease? A restaurant? A gym? A discussion group sponsored by the school? A long drive you are making together? How would you convey to your family member whether you want an intense discussion or a more casual conversation? Write your thoughts here.

Part IV: Evaluate Alternatives

Work with Alternatives

Don't be afraid to take one large step because you can't cross a chasm in two small leaps.

—Unknown

To Think About: Troubled relationships are often the culmination of many unresolved events that have simmered over time. Like a match to kindling, a single event can set off a series of actions that boil over into the family. But what if we had given more active attention to diffusing the situation earlier? What if we had practiced our skills of communication before the break?

The idea of meeting with our family member to resolve a dispute can make us sweat and question our level of preparedness and ability to accomplish the task. Today we will go through a practice session, using a different person and situation. This lesson's goal is to practice alternatives and select the ones that best suit the problem.

To Do: Choose a situation that brings up an issue to resolve. For example, you and your wife are trying to decide whether to buy a car, your nine-year-old daughter wants her ears pierced, your brother wants you to loan him money, or your spouse wants you to move from a part-time to a full-time job. Choose a topic you can address today.

Write the problem in the circle on the next page. Now, next to the picture of people, identify who else has been affected and how. At the picture of the open door, write down where and when you would like to have the discussion. Consider yesterday's guidelines as you plan. Finish the last two pictures after you talk.

Next to the final two pictures, write your evaluation of your listening skills and your positive body language during the conversation. Which of these skills do you still want to practice?

Part IV:
Evaluate Alternatives

Practice with a Friend

Be courteous to all, but intimate with few, and let those few be well tried before you give them your confidence. True friendship is a plant of slow growth, and must undergo and withstand the shocks of adversity.

—George Washington

DAY 13

To Think About: As we consider the problem we are facing, we may have concerns about whether we have adequately interpreted events, whether we have identified all of our alternatives, and whether we have planned for a meeting time and place that will foster a positive response. Prior to scheduling a meeting with your family member, you may want to set aside time to discuss the situation with a friend who has objective insights. For example, remember the story in Day 8 about your jealousy that your parents may have spent more on your sibling's wedding? If you took this situation to a friend, she may raise a number of relevant questions: Could the additional funds have been a loan? Or, your friend may ask you, "So what? Shouldn't you plan and enjoy your own wedding and be happy with your new life rather than dragging up unsupported allegations to blight the day?"

A friend may give you new perspectives on the problem and might have valuable suggestions for you to consider before you go forward.

➧ To Do: Consider a friend you might want to use as a mentor.

Write this person's name here: ______________________________

Rank this person on the following scale, from a low of "1" to a high of "3."

Characteristic		***Scale***	
1. Able to keep a confidence	1	2	3
2. Listens well to others	1	2	3
3. Generally has good relationships with others	1	2	3
4. Demonstrates a moral attitude toward life	1	2	3
5. Can remain detached from situation	1	2	3

So what do you think? Is this person a good choice? However, before involving your friend, keep in mind that discussing a significant family problem can cement a lasting relationship, or it may upset and worry the listener. Your friend may be concerned about being blamed if the situation becomes worse or if you don't take proffered advice. Work out the ground rules between you before disclosure.

Part IV: Evaluate Alternatives

Use a Referee

The significant problems we face cannot be solved at the same level of thinking we were at when we created them.

—Albert Einstein

DAY 14

To Think About: Depending on the situation and previous attempts you have made to reestablish a good relationship, you may want to have a third person mediate between you and your family member. This could be another family member, a therapist, or a religious leader. It must be someone you can both trust. Check with friends or neighbors, and select someone who has made a difference.

The person you select may or may not have professional training. You might want to choose a family member known for fairness, but be aware that regardless of whom you choose, the same problems as discussed yesterday in confiding with a friend can apply here.

You may want to try to work together on the selection. Talk through your criteria and work toward a consensus. The referee approach to resolution may be a positive step if it gets you talking together.

To Do: Select a test person and problem or use the real problem and the referee you have selected for this exercise. Discuss between you how you can best present your feelings to the referee. For example, you could each try writing down your feelings about the problem, how it has affected you, why preserving your relationship is important, and the amount of time and energy you are willing to invest in working toward a solution. Not surprisingly, writing helps to sort ideas, order priorities, and analyze cause-and-effect relationships. The act of writing itself may change your feelings and suggest new options.

So, how do you get started? You may want to do a timeline—an outline that shows the months or dates when certain events occurred. Explore the situation objectively, explain what happened, how you felt about it, and why you felt that way. Do it today. Just write. Don't worry about spelling, grammar, or punctuation. Just keep moving forward in time. You may not even choose to complete it in one sitting. Brainstorm what you want to write about, then for the next several days, put a few minutes aside each day to write. The writing itself does not substitute for actions you will take later, but it can help you prepare for it.

Do you need to share your writing? Not necessarily. You may choose to throw it away. It is the act of writing and organizing that is important, that clarifies your thinking. But you be the judge. In your situation, would it help to share a paragraph or a sentence or two from your writing in a card? What if you don't like to write? Then try using the same procedure, only instead of writing your thoughts down, record them onto tape. If you don't want others to read what you have written or listen to the tape, remember to put your materials away. Words taken out of context may be harmful to others.

As you see fit, you may share your writing with the referee or allow the referee to interview each person about their reaction to what the other person has said or written. This person's role is to help clarify feelings and the meaning behind the words being expressed.

Part V: Implement Your First Plan

Time to Talk

The man who goes alone can start today; but he who travels with another must wait till that other is ready.

—Henry David Thoreau, Walden (1854), I, Economy

To Think About: You have done two weeks of planning, and now it is time to start putting your plan into place. But before you do, go back to Day 1. Review why you wanted to address your problem at this time. Is an event driving your actions? Your family member may not have the same need to resolve the situation at this time. He or she may have other priorities—examinations, holiday planning, sick children. If you truly are interested in working on communication, start here by being flexible in your desire to get together.

To Do: Your activity for today is to contact your relative and try to set up a time to meet. If you are ready, do it now. If you need confidence boosting, you might want to try

- practicing the invitation aloud in the car
- practicing in front of a mirror
- talking through the invitation to your pet

The goal here is to strive to express yourself well and to set the framework for a cooperative, productive experience. Practicing aloud will help prepare you for a phone or personal invitation.

Now think back to your planning stage. You've been doing some preparation for today. Decide how you want to contact your family member and where you will meet. For fun, fill out the Family U Invitation below. Then make the call, write the note, or go see the person.

Family University Invitation

I, ______________________, would like to invite

____

to *(activity)* ______________________________

on *(date)* ______________ at *(time)* ______________.

Together, I hope we accomplish:

____

____

____

____

____

____

Part V:
Implement Your First Plan

Create a Partnership for Change

It does not take much strength to do things, but it requires great strength to decide what to do.

—Ivert Hubbard

To Think About: Conflict between individuals is normal. Usually, conflict is temporary and easily resolved, but at times we need new strategies and skills to restructure a severely damaged relationship. A first step might be to directly communicate to your family member that you value this relationship and want to save it. These important words can help set the foundation for reconciliation. You may even want to acknowledge that while you can't fix the original problem or go back to where you were, you can move on to a different relationship that may be just as satisfying.

Perhaps the best way to bring about lasting change is to form a partnership where you both are willing and dedicated to improving your relationship. Unilateral solutions usually won't work because there is only limited commitment. So how can you accomplish this goal? Try working as partners using a problem-solving method.

To Do: As you create your partnership for change, set the framework for the steps you will take together. Visualize yourself and your family member climbing a hill. You only have one rope, so sometimes one of you will go first, sometimes the other, or you both may be able to climb at the same time when the slope is less steep. Notice that the rope has knots in it. Stop at these knots and reflect. Think about how you will structure the conversation; can you identify what you want to happen at each step? Are there any other steps you want to include as you establish the framework for your discussion?

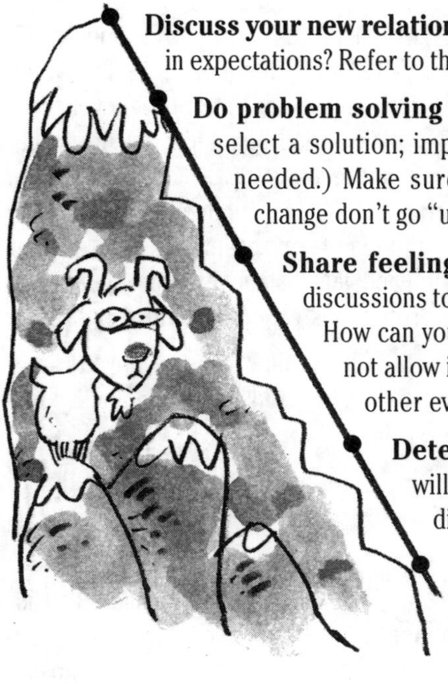

Discuss your new relationship. How will you resolve differences in expectations? Refer to the expectations discussed in Day 4.

Do problem solving together. (Brainstorm alternatives; select a solution; implement; evaluate; repeat process as needed.) Make sure that suggestions you each give for change don't go "unheard" or unevaluated.

Share feelings; don't blame. How will you limit discussions to the central problem without blaming? How can you keep the conversation focused and not allow it to be enlarged and result in blaming other events on this problem?

Determine the central problem. How will you resolve the issue if you each see a different central problem?

Agree that the two of you will set rules. Who else might try to become involved in the dispute?

Part V: Implement Your First Plan

How to Keep Talking

It is not best that we should all think alike; it is difference of opinion that makes horseraces.

—*Mark Twain (Samuel Clemens), from Pudd'nhead Wilson's Calendar (1894)*

To Think About: In the last lesson we talked about structuring your conversation so that you both are problem solvers, working toward mutual goals. Today we are going inside that conversation. So, you've set the time and date for discussion; you've worked through setting ground rules. Now it's time to talk. Perhaps you both make an opening statement of your feelings. Now what? You are aware of the unresolved issues and the hidden topics that need to come up. How can you keep the conversation flowing?

One way is, of course, to ask questions; we will discuss that approach in Day 27. But for today, we are going to explore a different technique. Remember when you were in school and you had sustained silent reading? You brought your own book to class and read to yourself for the whole period. That technique for teaching reading was started when it was observed that the way teachers would read a paragraph or two (or ask a student to read) then ask a question was actually counterproductive to comprehension and long-term retention. If the student were allowed to read for a longer period and gain a stronger understanding of the material, then both literal and interpretive mastery of the content improved.

To Do: You might want to practice a similar approach for your first reconciliation conversation. It requires you to use two skills: Sustained Active Listening and Sustained Explanation. Here is how it works:

- Each of you will speak without interruption for a period of time. Usually 3–5 minutes is an appropriate length. This allows the speaker to explain feelings in a broader context.
- The other person must be an active listener, noting the points made. The listener then gets the same time allotment to speak to issues raised or to explain his or her feelings. The rule is that only "I" messages may be spoken. "You" statements are not allowed.

- Determine the number of active listening responses in a row you want to make. When this point is reached, evaluate whether you want to continue or proceed to more informal conversation.

Before starting, you may also want to add a "repeating" rule. If the person speaking is repeating the exact information again, the listener can give a hand signal indicating a "deduct" (like a 15-second penalty). This keeps the conversation to new information.

Choose someone to practice this technique with today and note your observations.

____

____

____

____

____

____

____

____

Part V: Implement Your First Plan

Set Limits on Disagreements

Failure to prepare is preparing to fail.

—Unknown

DAY 18

To Think About: One reason many of us avoid conflict kinds of discussions is that they seem to get off track. We enter the conversation expecting to discuss one topic, and we exit not knowing what was discussed or resolved. The conversation takes on a will of its own, and we get buffeted around and sidetracked into unproductive areas. And so, you may want to consider adding other discussion rules or limits to those we discussed in Day 16.

To Do: You may have certain behaviors that could hinder a successful reconciliation meeting. As you read through the list, place a checkmark in the left column next to those that might derail conversations.

In the observations column, note those times you have exhibited this behavior and under what circumstances. In the second column, put a checkmark if you have seen your family member (FM) exhibit this behavior.

Me	FM	Example	Observations
		Abruptly end meetings without a plan	
		Always insist that yours is the only right interpretation	
		Defend your own actions	
		Blame others	
		Bring in what other friends or relatives have said	
		Continue the conversation in front of others	
		Decide, without checking, the next steps or acceptable alternatives	
		Demand to set meeting times/topics	
		Make inflammatory "below the belt" statements	
		Link current situation to old grievances	
		Play psychologist; assume you know what the family member is thinking	
		Repeat the same point over and over	
		Share the conversation in an unflattering way with others	
		Speak in absolutes — "you always"; "you never"	
		Speak loudly when excited	
		Threaten violence or retribution	
		Use an intimidating tone	
		Use body language that signals resistance	
		Withdraw and refuse to talk	

Monitor your own tendency to use these negative behaviors. You might also bring up some of these topics to discuss during your rule-setting conversation so that you have mutual expectations for behaviors.

Part V: Implement Your First Plan

The Power of Praise

Kind words can be short and easy to speak,
but their echoes are truly endless.

—*Mother Teresa*

To Think About: The conversation you will soon have with your family member has great potential for healing. One way you can plan ahead for that to occur is to think positively about the person and plan kind words you want to say. But just giving your family member a general compliment will not achieve your healing objective. It may be brushed aside as hollow and void of real honesty. In contrast, a compliment tied to an action has a greater chance of being noticed, appreciated, and remembered.

For example, compare these two statements:

- Your report card is better this quarter.
- You have worked so hard studying this quarter. You must be pleased that your report card reflects all your efforts. I certainly am proud of you.

Each of us wants to be seen as a worthy individual, capable of love and caring. So as you attempt to resolve your dispute, be sure that you focus on one area, rather than a general commendation of the other person. Praise is a powerful motivator and energizer if offered sincerely.

To Do: Think about the words of praise you might want to use during your meeting. Visualize your family member smiling at you, pleased with what you are saying. Now with a picture of the person in mind, write each letter of your family member's name in the boxes at the left. After each letter, write a praise phrase about the person beginning with that letter. For example, if the name were TOM, I might write for "T"—Takes time to play with kids.

Complete this phrase, I am proud of you because you ...

- ☐ ____________________
- ☐ ____________________
- ☐ ____________________
- ☐ ____________________
- ☐ ____________________
- ☐ ____________________
- ☐ ____________________
- ☐ ____________________
- ☐ ____________________

If, in your meeting, you want to compliment your family member, you will have these examples ready by just thinking of the letters of the person's name.

Part V: Implement Your First Plan

Devise an Action Vocabulary

Remember, people will judge you by your actions, not your intentions. You may have a heart of gold —but so does a hard-boiled egg.

—Unknown

❦ **TO THINK ABOUT:** As you go forward with plans for your conversation you also need to be thinking beyond this event. What outcomes do you want, and what actions will be needed to accomplish them? We have already discussed a number of action words:

brainstorm
problem solve
listen
praise
share

We discussed these action words as part of the meeting you are planning with your relative. Think beyond this point. What action words will guide you as you look toward the future? Words such as "evaluate, plan, thank, love, release, cry, or forgive" may come to mind.

To Do: Suppose you had a camera and you loaded a roll of film that had twelve pictures for you to take after your first meeting with your relative. Imagine what you are doing and draw a picture or write in one action word for each frame on your negative strip. Fill in as many as possible.

Part V: Implement Your First Plan

And If You're Both Right . . .

Even if you're on the right track,
you'll get run over if you just sit there.

—Will Rogers

DAY 21

To Think About: Sometimes when we are involved in a dispute, we go over and over our positions in our minds until we view every interpretation as fact, every inference as a significant message aimed at us. And, indeed, our position may be the right and only one to take, such as not tolerating a family member's foul language or offensive behavior. At other times, valid arguments may counter our positions. The goal is to know the difference and to separate out logic and emotion.

To Do: As attorneys prepare for court, they must know their position and also be able to anticipate the position of the opposing party. In a less structured way, we can work through a similar process.

First, briefly state the problem: College age child refuses to honor curfew when home.

Next, state your position in the left column and your family member's position in the right column.

	My Position		***Family Member's Position***
✔	Curfew has always been midnight	+	I have no curfew at college and handle it
+	Nothing you need to be involved in after midnight	+	Parties sometimes last late
✔	You need to be a role model for your brothers	-	My brothers should not have a curfew either

Then put a "+" if it is a strong position, a "✔" for an OK position, and a "–" for a false position. Now, circle your strongest position and your family member's strongest argument.

You may have marked the ratings differently, but you can see in this example how you can take some of the emotion out of the disagreement by analyzing the positions. If your main concern is whom he is with when he is out late, maybe you need to communicate this rather than the midnight rule. If he is at a party where you know his friends, is there time latitude? On the other hand, your young adult may have a valid position in that he handles his schedule nine months of the year without parental supervision and can do the same at home. However, he may need to rethink what being courteous and accommodating have to do with creating new stepping stones to your future family relationships.

Evaluate your problem now using this tool and looking for areas of accommodation. You might want to try writing your positions on paper, ranking them in order of their importance to you, then exchanging papers and seeing if you can defend the opposite position . . . looking for areas of agreement.

___

___

___

___

___

___

___

Part VI:
Consider the Responses
Many Faces

I love the man that can smile in trouble, that can gather strength from distress and grow brave by reflection.
—Thomas Paine

DAY 22

To Think About: This is the first day of "Consider the Responses." By this point, you should have had your first meeting. You will now need to sort out your observations and assess your progress.

To Do: Summarize the meeting.

Now analyze the situation from the perspectives of three roles you play (e.g., as a businessman, as a coach, as a teacher, as a religious teacher).

On the line above each box label your role and describe inside each box how you would view the situation differently from that perspective.

Which perspective seems the most valid to you, or can you incorporate ideas from all three? If failure or rejection were part of your first meeting, consider what response a person in each role might make, to restart the process.

Part VI: Consider the Responses

Types of Negotiations

Let your heart guide you. It whispers, so listen closely.
—The Land Before Time

DAY 23

To Think About: As you consider the next steps you and your family member will take in the reconciliation process, you may start to see this as a business negotiation. Everyone gives a bit and eventually you end with a "win-win" situation. However, viewing the outcome in this way misses part of the very essence of reconciliation. This approach usually results in compromise: you give up something in exchange for your partner giving up something; you both end up with a part of what you want. This type of negotiation may cut a deal, but may not meet the felt needs. The underlying emotions that precipitated the problem may go unresolved.

Think back to your meeting. How did it go? Are you resolving the issue using a compromise approach only? Did you try to meet emotional needs? Did you try to find areas of consensus? In broadening our discussion of negotiations, also consider how similar or different your "walk away" position (the "deal-breaker") might be if you considered the issue from a business perspective or a family perspective only. How would that affect your discussions and actions?

To Do: Blend the problem you are having with your family member with negotiations. Suppose you are a business negotiator bringing this conflict to a successful conclusion. What would your win-win position be, what strategies would you use, at what point would you walk away? Now consider the same when your goal is meeting the felt or emotional needs.

Compromise-Based Contract

Win-win position is ______________________________

____

Strategies to use are ______________________________

____

____

Walk away position is ______________________________

____

Needs-Based Contract

Win-win position is ______________________________

____

Strategies to use are ______________________________

____

____

Walk away position is ______________________________

____

If you have trouble with this activity, it may be because you are dealing with a conflict of values, such as when an unmarried brother and his girlfriend want to share a room while visiting you—you think it is morally wrong and don't want to set a bad example for your children. You may want to combine the two approaches; welcome the couple into your home but take a value-based position and have them stay at the local hotel.

Part VI: Consider the Responses

From the Other Side of the Table

Nothing is easier than self-deceit. For what each man wishes, that he also believes to be true.

—Demosthenes

TO THINK ABOUT: In our third day of Consider the Responses, we are going to focus on assessing your actions during the reconciliation meeting. We will assume that you are pleased with your interactions in certain areas and have identified other areas you wish to work on. Today is an opportunity for mirror reflections. We will concentrate on how you were perceived by your family member.

TO DO: Think about the meeting with your family member. The two of you have spent some time together, across a table, strolling in a park, or whatever. For today's first activity, put yourself in your family member's place and picture yourself. What do you see? What do you hear? Pick out four things you think you did well, then select two areas you would like to improve. Make bars and rate your performance on these bar charts.

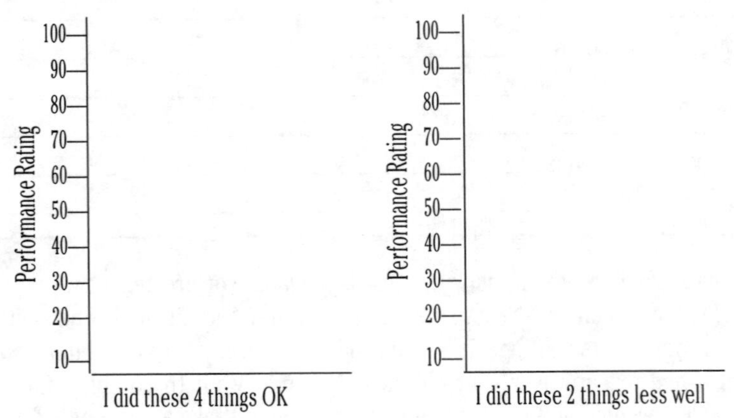

Now for your second activity, talk to someone in your family about a problem. After the conversation, invite your family member to talk about the process the two of you used. Ask questions about your performance and write the observations here.

____

____

____

____

____

____

How closely did you match your perceptions of performance with how this second family member perceived you? You may find that the areas you identified as a weakness, the other person identified as a strength.

Conclusions?

____

____

____

____

____

____

Part VI:
Consider the Responses

Ancient History

Things that are done, it is needless to speak about . . .
things that are past, it is needless to blame.

—Confucius

To Think About: In spite of your efforts to keep to discussion guidelines, old unresolved topics may have come up during your meeting with your family member. Even if they did not come up in the conversation, these topics and events are probably in the back of your mind, festering. It is human nature to want to hold on to these grievances. If someone hurts us, we can say, "Well, remember when you . . ." It's part of the grand scorekeeping of life and may be a habit we have developed as part of our social interactions. We keep one foot in the present and one foot planted firmly in the past.

If we are always playing, "Got you first; got you last" we are concentrating on the game and not on the message of partnering and growing in harmony together as a family. It is time to let the past rest, to end the blame, to take a step. Drag your foot from the past and plant it in the future.

To Do: Let go of old grievances. Here is a trash can with many pieces of crumpled papers inside. Take a moment and write on those crumpled sheets of paper old hurts and old events with your family member that you want to forgive and forget. You may need to go back in time a bit to get them all identified. For some you may only need to write a word or two, while others require a longer explanation. Trash the old hurts now.

Anytime you are tempted to bring these topics up in the future, resist. Remember you put them in the trash and they are gone. You can't retrieve them or keep score with them any more.

Part VII: Implement Your Second Plan

Lighten Up

The human race has one really effective weapon, and that is laughter.

—Mark Twain

❦ **To Think About:** Today we will consider another golden oldie saying: "You make yourself about as happy as you intend to be." Think about this message. It's not saying you will be happy tomorrow or the next day when this problem or that problem is resolved. It's not saying anyone else, or anything else can make you happy. You have the power and ability within yourself to be happy—when you decide to be. And, conversely, when you don't decide to be happy, you may feel the anxieties and frustrations of daily living more acutely because you are looking at life from the dark side. Indeed, even resolving the conflict successfully with your family member may not make you feel happy, unless you intend to be.

While few of us may consider ourselves comedians, we can do much to present a happy countenance to others and enliven the lives of those around us. First, even though you may be unhappy with your family member, don't turn it into a catastrophe. Don't whine and complain endlessly to others about the situation. Don't grind conversations to a halt with stories of gloom and doom. Don't set yourself up as a martyr for all you are forced to bear.

However, do applaud yourself for the steps you have taken at reconciliation. Do lighten up and count your blessings. Do try to lighten the load of someone else.

➧ **To Do:** First, on at least ten occasions today, when others approach to speak to you, smile at them before they speak. Watch their reactions and record your observations here.

____

____

____

____

____

Second, make an effort to tell a joke, share a cartoon, or point out a humorous irony in life. Record the reactions of people around you here.

____

____

____

____

Third, give your day a happiness rating. Did your efforts to be happy make you feel better? Did people ask you why you were in a good mood (surely a message for you there!)? Did you catch yourself slipping into unhappy thoughts and decide to "intend to be happy" instead?

____

____

Fourth, set up your second reconciliation meeting and remember to use these "lightening up" skills.

Part VII: Implement Your Second Plan

Artful Use of Questions

Good questions outrank easy answers.

—Paul A. Samuelson

DAY 27

❦ **To Think About:** We have talked about listening skills. Today we will focus on question asking skills. You've been in the situation where you have felt like you're being grilled, questions coming one after another, and you're not sure the answer to one question was heard before the next one was asked. Questioning is an art, and you need to be an artist to make sure you ask the right questions—ones that get you to the crux of the problem with your family member, ones that reveal whether or not the solution is meaningful to the other person.

You may want to monitor the amount of time you are talking and practice asking questions rather than spending so much time talking about yourself. One of your goals is to not dominate the conversation, but to listen carefully and ask the questions that will help you understand your family member's point of view.

➧ **To Do:** Try a variation of the listening exercise we did on Day 6. On that day, we explored a listening activity where each person spoke for a period of uninterrupted time. Similar time rules govern today's activity, but the listener can ask clarifying questions to get the person speaking to expand on their feelings. The listener may not offer solutions, give opinions, or challenge the accuracy of statements. Examples of questions are:

> Why was that important to you?
> How did it make you feel?
> Why was the timing important to you?
> What did you learn from that?

You may also paraphrase your understanding, and check it with the speaker for accuracy. "What I hear you saying is . . ." "Have I understood you correctly?"

This activity is not geared to present your position, but to make sure you have adequately understood what was said to you. Today have a conversation or watch a controversial TV show with someone in your family. Ask clarifying questions for a period of time without inserting your observations, feelings, or conclusions.

Record your thoughts here. Was this technique of asking clarifying questions comfortable for you? Are you at ease with gathering information or did you find it difficult to frame questions? Notice that if you start a sentence with "How" or "Why," it is easier to phrase the clarifying question.

___

___

___

___

___

___

___

___

___

___

Part VII: Implement Your Second Plan

Seeing the Bigger Picture

To see what is right and not to do it, is want of courage.
—Confucius Analects

DAY 28

❦ **To Think About:** Over the past month, we have narrowed our focus and shone a bright light on one relationship in your family. We have concentrated our attention on the relationship between you and a family member. But families are made up of many two-person relationships, each of which need nurturing. Today, step back and view the larger landscape of your relationships. Is this one relationship an aberration, an unusual occurrence in your life, or are other relationships not flourishing as well? What activities can you be doing now to avoid misunderstandings and to strengthen communication? Family communication is like a muscle—use it or lose it. It takes analysis to see the pathway of what you can do and energy to carry it out, but you have demonstrated that you are a person of courage and initiative.

➤ **To Do:** In the activity below, the circle in the center is for your name. Around the circle are a number of spokes, each one for an adult family member close to you. Add more spokes if you like. Write family members' names on the lines, then in the small boxes; rate the relationship as it now exists. Use a "+" for a strong relationship, a "✔" for an OK relationship, and a "–" for a poor relationship.

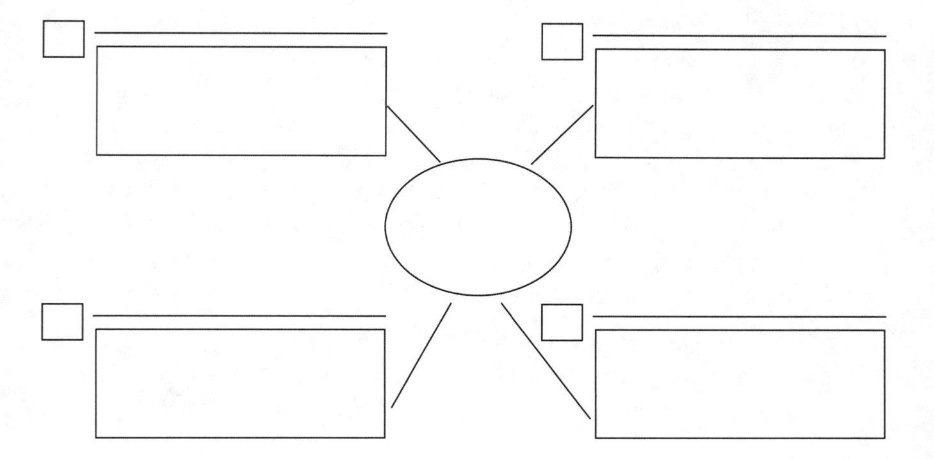

Now in each of the larger blocks write activities you can do with this person. For example, if you have children away from home, can you meet them for lunch once a week, invite them over for dinner once a month, start a family book club, buy season tickets at sports events, and so on?

How do you think you are doing as you step back and view the larger picture of your relationships? Record your thoughts here.

____

____

____

____

____

Part VIII: Achieve Long-Term Change

Be Gentle with Yourself

Beyond a wholesome discipline, be gentle with yourself. You are a child of the universe, no less than the trees and the stars; you have a right to be here. And whether or not it is clear to you, no doubt the universe is unfolding as it should.

—*Desiderata, 1692*

To Think About: You may find that this reconciliation process is going less well than you had hoped for. The progress may be slow, the conversations may seem stilted, the outcome may not be obvious. You may blame yourself for the lack of progress. You need to stop, regroup, and "be gentle with yourself." Even with good intentions, many other forces may be at work, ones over which you have no control. Keep yourself on track by working at open communication with your family member. Continue to talk, but make sure your conversations do not include gossip, rumors, and secondhand information. This type of conversation can lead to misunderstandings and derail your efforts.

To Do: Over the last month, you have tried many new approaches to problem solving in one particular relationship. Today, look around your family at other two-person relationships that are less nurturing than they could be. Choose one relationship. Then go to each person and suggest one way that communications with the other person in the relationship could be enhanced. You might choose one of the activities we did together or a technique you have used in the past. Put your ideas in the suggestion box. The suggestions for each person need not be the same.

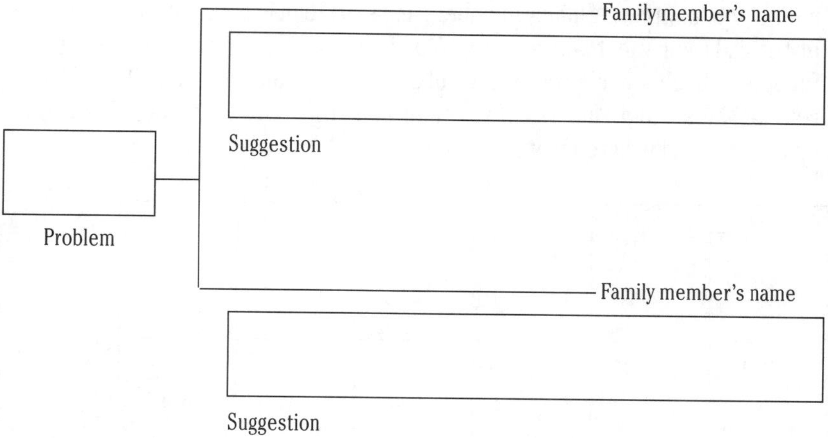

Family member's name

Suggestion

Problem

Family member's name

Suggestion

Select one suggestion from each box and talk with each of your family members today. But in the days to come, don't hover or insist on your advice being taken. Be a "gentle" peacemaker, available if you're needed.

Part VIII:
Achieve Long-Term Change

Commitment

Unless commitment is made, there are only promises and hopes . . . but no plans.

—Peter Drucker

DAY 30

❦ **To Think About:** During the past month, we have done a lot of brainstorming and taken steps toward reconciliation, but it is only a beginning. To sustain it, plans and commitment are needed. In the business world, those with services keep in touch with clients and plan ahead in a tickler file to call contacts periodically to keep each relationship strong. If you have small children, you keep detailed calendars of practices, games, and lessons. If you are in school, you are always balancing time in a dynamic, changing environment. But what about our adult family members? Do we give them the same emphasis or do they take leftover time? How are we modeling our commitment to family?

➧ **To Do:** Quickly fill in the dates on the calendar below, then get on the phone or talk with your family members and start to plan some activities. Include phone calls you want to make to check on family members, extended family get-togethers, birthday celebrations . . . all the activities that go into building strong relationships and memories. If you think you don't have time, then don't complain if you feel isolated from the family.

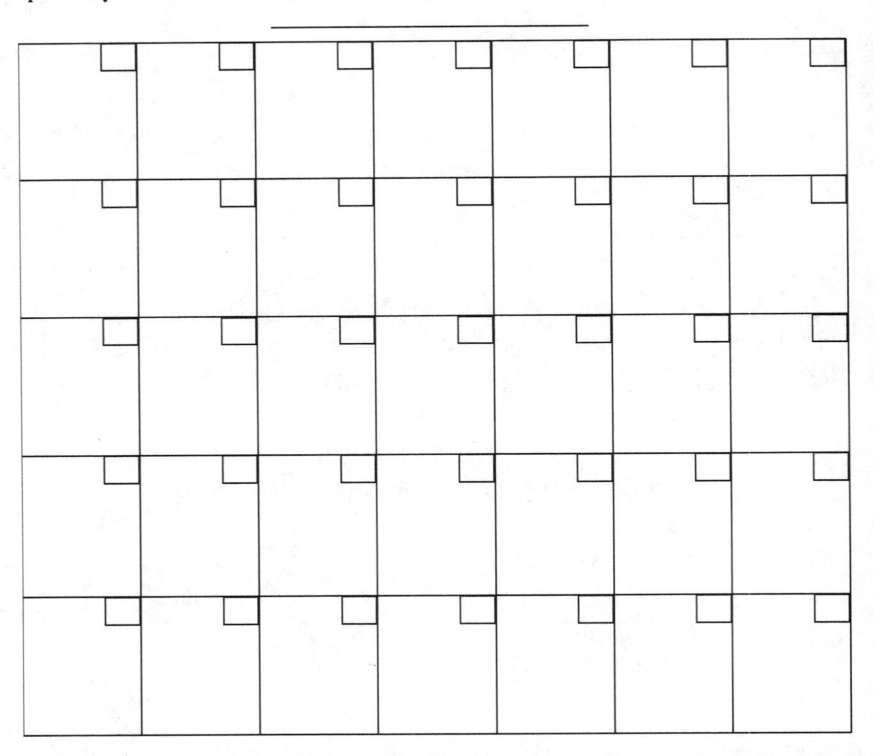

Display your calendar prominently so others can see your commitment to family. As you do the activities this month, plan subsequent activities and get them logged on the next month's calendar. At the end of the month, go back to Day 29 and look at your important family relationships. Try to estimate how much time you gave to each. Are you achieving a balance? Is your model encouraging other family members to emphasize family relationships?

Part VIII: Achieve Long-Term Change

Conclusion

Good people are good because they've come to wisdom through failure.

—William Saroyan

Congratulations! You have taken a troubled relationship with a family member and worked in a consistent manner to improve it. Instead of complaining and worrying, you have taken action and used the situation as an opportunity for personal growth. Take pride in the fact that you have assessed the problem; you have moved through the necessary steps toward a positive change, and you have been open to analyzing and changing your behavior to make communication more effective.

Remember that the steps you have used are not static. At times in the relationship, you may want to revisit the problem-solving steps. Consider this first time through as a benchmark. It identifies where you are at this period in time. You can measure your future progress against it.

In the Introduction, we discovered that families and the love that binds them exist beyond the growing up years. They are the nourishment of our adult lives. They encourage dynamic relationships, always growing and changing but remaining stable in their enduring quest to comfort and be comforting. You have engaged in that process this month, acknowledging the past and building toward greater intimacy in the future. Your efforts are worthy of praise.

We close our thirty days together with a poem about the enduring nature of families.

That Family of Mine

They won't leave me alone, that family of mine,
They're there when I start to stray off the track.
With a nudge and a tug and a firm warning—
  Our family don't do that,
  Child, get yourself right.
  You listen and learn
  And life will get right.

And so I bounce between uncle and aunt,
Learning the lessons of family lore . . .
That nobody's there for you like your family is.
That nobody loves you like your family does.

And then as an adult I get pulled by the world
Which whispers, "Your family is a thing of the past.
Grow up, move on, choose friends over family."
But those teachings of old, they're not easily dismissed,
They laugh at the notion that family's not needed,
With a wink and a nod, they beckon me back.

Our family don't stray,
Child, get yourself right.
You listen and learn
And life will get right.

They won't leave me alone, that family of mine,
And their love sustains me through good and bad times.

Enrollment in the annual curriculum brings 16 family-building tools to your kitchen table.